The Big Bug

Based on the story
"The Metamorphosis" by Franz Kafka
Adapted by Michael Leviton

SCHOLASTIC INC.

New York Toronto London Auckland Sydney
Mexico City New Delhi Hong Kong Buenos Aires

Illustrations by
Gris Grimly

Text copyright © 2005 by Scholastic Inc.
Illustrations copyright © 2005 by Gris Grimly.
All rights reserved. Published by Scholastic Inc.
Printed in the U.S.A.

ISBN 0-439-12407-7
(meets NASTA specifications)

3   4   5   6   7   8   9   10   23   13 12 11 10 09 08 07 06

Contents

Sometimes people change. Sometimes people even change overnight.

1 A Bug Morning

One morning, Gregor Samsa awoke from a bad dream. He opened his eyes and lifted his head. He saw that he had changed overnight. His belly had become big, round, and hard. He now had lots of thin, little legs that waved and **twitched**. He had turned into a giant bug!

"This is strange," Gregor thought. "It must be a dream." He tried to wake up. But it was not a dream.

Gregor tried to move his huge, heavy body. But no matter how he tried, he just rolled onto his back again. He could not get out of bed. Then he noticed the clock.

Gregor saw that he had changed. He had turned into a giant bug!

"Oh no!" Gregor thought. "It's nine o'clock! I'm two hours late for work!"

He knew that Mr. K would yell at him. Mr. K was Gregor's boss. Mr. K ordered Gregor around and made fun of him. Gregor hated Mr. K. He made Gregor feel like a bug.

And now Gregor really *was* a bug!

Why does Gregor feel like a bug when he's at work?

Gregor has a lot on his mind. And now his family is starting to bug him.

2 Voices Through the Door

Gregor heard a knock on his bedroom door. "Gregor," his mother said. "It's nine o'clock! You're late!"

Gregor tried to say, "Yes, I know. I'm getting up." But a horrible noise came out of his mouth. It did not sound like talking. It sounded like someone throwing up.

Mrs. Samsa could not understand Gregor's noise. So, she just said, "That's good, Gregor!" Then she walked back to join her husband and daughter.

The Samsas had been sitting at the kitchen table for an hour. Their dirty breakfast plates still sat in front of them.

They were very nervous. Gregor was late. He could get fired! And if he got fired, the Samsas would starve!

Mr. and Mrs. Samsa didn't have jobs. And Gregor's sister, Grete, was too young to work. She was only 15. So Gregor supported his whole family. He paid for their food, clothes, and home.

Gregor's father knocked on the door. "Gregor," he said, "What's wrong?"

Grete came to the door too. She said, "Gregor? Aren't you well?"

Gregor said, "I'm just getting up!" But his voice came out as a long, loud bark.

"Please open the door," Grete said.

But how could Gregor open the door? He couldn't turn a doorknob! Not with those ugly, twitching legs!

Then, Gregor heard the doorbell ring. "It's my boss, Mr. K!" Gregor said to himself. His little legs waved faster.

Gregor knows he has to get out of bed. He can't be a bed bug forever!

3 Gregor Gets Out of Bed

"Gregor," his father said through the door. "Mr. K is here. He wants to know why you are not at work."

"Gregor, I want an **explanation**!" Mr. K shouted.

"The poor boy must be sick," Gregor's mother said.

"Gregor," his father said angrily. "Open the door!"

Mr. K said, "Gregor, come out right now, or I will fire you!"

The Samsas all turned pale.

Gregor tried to explain. "But sir," he said. "Please just give me another minute. I'll get up. I'm not feeling well. It's funny. Last night I felt fine! I was not sick at all." But Gregor's speech did not sound like speech at all.

"Did you understand a word of that?" Mr. K asked Mr. Samsa.

Mrs. Samsa said, "Gregor must be very sick. Grete, call the doctor!"

Gregor now rocked his body as hard as he could. He flopped out of bed and hit the door with a loud crash. He heard his family scream.

Then Gregor tried to turn the doorknob with his mouth. When he bit down, brown **fluid** poured from his mouth.

Finally, Gregor got the door open. He stood there, a giant bug, in front of his family and Mr. K.

Mr. K shouted, "Oh!" He covered his mouth with his hand. He started to back away slowly. Gregor's mother screamed and burst into tears.

Finally, Gregor got the door open. His family and Mr. K screamed.

Mr. Samsa held up his fists. He was ready to fight.

Gregor tried to calm everyone down. "I'm ready for work now," he said. "I know I'm still a bit sick. But I can't let that stop me!"

Everyone stared as the giant bug seemed to cough at them. "So, I'll just get dressed, and we'll go to the office," Gregor said.

But Mr. K was already out the door. In fact, he had left in a huge hurry. He had even forgotten his hat and cane. Now Gregor was sure Mr. K would fire him. Who would want to work with a giant bug?

Then, Gregor smelled something. Food! He was very hungry. He opened his mouth and **drooled**. His mother screamed again.

His father picked up the cane Mr. K had left behind. He poked Gregor with it. He hit Gregor harder and harder. Gregor backed into the bedroom. His father slammed the door shut.

Gregor looked at himself and saw big brown marks all over. And when he walked, he left a trail behind him. The trail was a mix of brown blood and sticky stuff from his feet.

How do you think Gregor's family will treat him now that he's a bug?

The Samsas try to get used to living with a giant bug. But how can they?

4 Gregor the Pest

Gregor woke up and **realized** he had fainted. He did not know how much time had passed. His legs hurt. He looked down and saw that a few of them had stopped moving. They hung from his body like pieces of spaghetti.

Gregor worried about his family. Without him, they would have no money at all. They would have to live on the streets! Grete would have to go to work!

Gregor spent that day and night in his room. He was hungry and worried. Then, early in the morning, Grete came to give him food.

A month passed, and Grete fed him every day. When Gregor heard her turning the doorknob, he always hid under the bed. That way, she would never have to look at him.

Gregor listened to his family through the door. They did not know that Gregor could understand them. So, they talked about him as if he were not there.

Gregor often heard Grete and his mother crying all night. His mother would say, "Poor Gregor! It must feel terrible to be a bug!"

Grete would try to comfort her. She would say, "Gregor will get better soon! Today when I fed him, he looked more like himself!" But this just made Mrs. Samsa cry harder.

Mr. Samsa didn't cry. He would shout, "Gregor is nothing but a **pest**!"

Gregor's mother and sister try to make his room bug-friendly.

5 A Gift for Gregor

Gregor spent every day in his room. For fun, he'd walk on the walls and ceiling. He left sticky stuff wherever he crawled. Gregor's sister **noticed** this sticky stuff. So, she knew he liked to crawl around. This gave her an idea.

Grete told her mother, "Gregor's furniture gets in his way! We should empty his room. That way, he'll have more room to play."

"You're right," Mrs. Samsa said. "Poor Gregor needs room to crawl."

Gregor heard his mother and sister talking. He became excited. "No furniture!"

For fun, Gregor walked on the walls and ceiling of his room.

Gregor jumped onto the desk. His mother saw him and fainted.

he thought. "I'll have so much room! That sounds great!"

Grete knocked on Gregor's door. She knew Gregor couldn't answer. She just wanted to give him time to hide.

Gregor hid under the bed. Grete and Mrs. Samsa walked into his room. They picked up his desk. Then Mrs. Samsa stopped.

"Wait," she said. "Maybe we *shouldn't* take away the furniture. Gregor might think we've given up hope that he'll get better!"

That made Gregor think. Maybe they *did* think he'd be a bug forever!

Gregor realized something else. He *liked* the furniture. It reminded him that he wasn't just a bug. He was a human trapped in a bug's body. What if he didn't have any furniture? He'd just be a bug in a dirty, empty room.

Gregor wanted to stop Grete and his mother. He ran out from under the bed. He jumped onto his desk, **startling** his mother.

His mother screamed, "Oh Gregor! No! No!" She fainted on the floor.

Grete dragged her mother out of the room. She looked at Gregor with **disgust**.

Gregor followed them into the living room. He wanted to help his mother.

Just then, Gregor's father came home. He screamed when he saw Gregor in the middle of the room. Then he saw his wife lying on the couch. Mr. Samsa could not tell what had happened. But he was sure it was Gregor's fault.

Mr. Samsa ran over to Gregor. He lifted his foot over Gregor's back. He was about to step on him! But just in time, Gregor ran to the corner!

Then, Mr. Samsa grabbed some apples and started throwing them. Every apple that hit Gregor felt like a brick. One of the apples hit him so hard that it stuck in his back. Gregor could feel his brown bug blood **trickle** down his side.

Mr. Samsa lifted his foot. He was about to step on Gregor!

Mrs. Samsa woke up. She grabbed her husband's arm. "Please stop!" she begged. "You'll kill him! That's Gregor, our son!"

"That dirty, slimy thing is not Gregor! How could it be Gregor?" Mr. Samsa yelled. He threw the apples even harder. "That thing probably ate Gregor! That bug is just pretending to be our son!"

Gregor ran into his room and pulled the door shut with his mouth.

Why did Mr. Samsa attack Gregor?

It's not easy living with a giant bug.
Gregor's family has had enough!

6 Bug Off!

After that, Grete stopped cleaning Gregor's room. And she only fed him once a week. The bedroom got very dirty. When Gregor crawled around, dirt and pieces of food stuck to his body. He was covered in crumbs, dust, bits of apple, and his dried brown blood. He looked disgusting.

Gregor heard his family talk about moving away. "We need a smaller apartment. We can't pay for a big one anymore," Mr. Samsa said.

"But what about Gregor?" asked Grete.

"You and Gregor could share a room," Mrs. Samsa said.

Grete jumped out of her seat. "What!?" she said.

Before anyone could say any more, Mr. Samsa said, "Nonsense. The bug must go! That's all there is to it."

"No!" said Mrs. Samsa, crying.

"Let's keep Gregor and take in another family to share the rent," Grete said.

So, they found another family to share the apartment. But the Samsas kept Gregor's door shut. They didn't want the new family to know about Gregor.

Then one night Grete was playing her violin for the new family. Gregor liked the music. So, he opened his door a bit to listen.

The daughter of the new family saw two giant **antennae** sticking out from behind the door. She screamed, "What's that?"

The father of the family opened the door and saw Gregor. He shouted, "Aaaaah!"

"Don't be afraid," Grete said. "That's my brother! His name is Gregor!"

"What's that?" the daughter screamed, pointing at Gregor.

The father quickly slammed the door. "Your brother?" he asked.

"You let that bug live here?" the mother asked.

"We won't live with a giant bug!" the father said.

So, they packed their bags and left.

After they shut the door, Grete got upset. "Things can't go on like this!" she said. "How will we pay our bills? We've tried to be nice to Gregor. But he ruins everything."

"Grete, don't say things like that about your brother!" Mrs. Samsa said.

Grete went on. "Maybe Father is right!" she said. "Maybe that bug is not Gregor! It can't be Gregor! Gregor would not want us to live with a giant bug! Gregor would have gone away by now."

Gregor couldn't stand to hear his family speak about him like this. He crawled out of his room. His family looked at him in disgust.

He forgave them for wanting to get rid of him. Gregor knew it wasn't easy to live with a giant bug.

So, he decided to go back to his room. But it was hard to turn around. He was out of breath. He felt very weak. His room seemed very far away.

Then, the pain in Gregor's back and legs went away. He thought of his family and felt love for them. He did not want to cause them any more trouble. He wanted to leave them alone. But he had nowhere else to go. Then, Gregor died right there on the floor.

How do you think the Samsas feel now that Gregor is dead?

The Samsas won't let a giant dead bug ruin their day!

7 A Lovely Afternoon

When Gregor's family saw him die, Grete and Gregor's mother started to cry.

"Don't waste your tears," Gregor's father said. "That bug is dead! We can live again! We'll work hard and be happy."

Then Grete pointed out the window. "Look how sunny it is outside," she said. "Let's go for a walk. We'll put the bug in the trash later."

So the Samsas stepped over Gregor's dead body and went outside. It was a beautiful day. They spent a lovely afternoon together. And they forgot all about the ugly dead bug in their apartment.

The Samsas stepped over Gregor's dead body and went outside.

Glossary

antennae *(noun)* feelers on the head of an insect

disgust *(noun)* feeling of being grossed out *(related word: disgusting)*

drooled *(verb)* let spit drip from the mouth *(related words: drool, drooling)*

explanation *(noun)* a reason or excuse *(related word: explain)*

fluid *(noun)* some kind of liquid, like water

noticed *(verb)* saw *(related word: notice)*

pest *(noun)* an insect; also an annoying person

realized *(verb)* understood

startling *(verb)* surprising and scaring *(related word: startle)*

trickle *(verb)* to flow slowly in a thin stream

twitched *(verb)* made small, quick movements *(related words: twitch, twitching)*